DISCOVERING

Executive Editors
Cameron John Yerian, M.A.
Margaret A. Yerian, M.A.

Art Director
Thomas Petiet, M.F.A.

Designer
Cameron John Yerian

Senior Editors for _DISCOVERING_
Nancy Muhlbach, M.A.
Jerry Gillmore, B.A.

Contributors
Mary Rush, M.F.A.
Sharon Irvine, B.A.
Mary White, B.A.
Edith Wolter, B.S.
Susan Keezer
Virginia Foster, A.B.

Editorial Assistant
Phoebe A. Yerian

Readability Consultants
Donald E.P. Smith, Ph.D.
School of Education
University of Michigan

Judith K. Smith, Ph.D.
University of Michigan

Instructional Development Consultant
Joel B. Fleming, M.A.
Instructional Development & Technology
Michigan State University

Synectics Consultant
Gershom Clark Morningstar, M.A.
President, Wolverine-Morningstar Media

Library Consultant
Noel Winkler, M.A.L.S.
Lecturer, Children's Literature
Elementary Librarian, Media Center
School of Education
University of Michigan

DISCOVERING

Me & the Rest of the Universe

Creative Activities...Program

CHILDRENS PRESS/GROLIER ENTERPRISES

A word to Parents:

All of the activities in this book have been successfully performed by children. The ease with which these have been accomplished has varied with the age and skill development of each individual child. A project which is both safe and easy for a twelve-year-old, may require adult supervision for a child of eight. Basic rules of safety apply to all children and should be scrupulously followed in whatever they do. Only you, the parents, can determine the ease with which your children can successfully and safely perform any activity. Only you can determine the degree of guidance your children will require.

This is not a book to *read*—it is a book to *do*.

We have designed this book to be enjoyed by all ages. We hope that it will provide many hours of pleasure for you and your children.

The Editors

Prepared and produced by Y⁴ Design
for
Regensteiner Publishing Enterprises, Inc.

Contents

Hearing

MAKE a tin can telephone to help you talk to friends and to hear them.

GET 2 clean tin cans, 1 long piece of string, and some wax.

MAKE a small hole in each of the cans. **USE** a nail or sharp object to make the hole. Be careful.

PUT the string through the hole and tie a knot in it.

WAX the string to make it stiff.

GIVE one phone to your friend.

STRETCH the string tight and talk into the can.

LET your friend talk. What can you hear?

TRY using wire in your phone instead of string. Does string or wire carry sound better?

You can send messages from one room to another on your private telephone.

Smelling

TRY to fool a friend.

GET a blindfold, a slice of apple, and a slice of pear.

BLINDFOLD your friend. Let him smell the pear as you feed him the apple.

TRY this with other similar food.

LET him fool you now.

Tasting

Do parts of your tongue tell you when something is sweet, sour, or salty?

USE a small spoon to put liquids on your tongue.

USE lemon juice. Try also sugar, salt, baking soda, and vanilla in water.

TASTE each liquid on the tip of your tongue. Does the tip of your tongue tell you things are sweet, sour, or salty?

TRY each liquid on the side of your tongue.

TRY the back of your tongue now.

DON'T use anything but foods.

Touching

BLINDFOLD a group of friends. Have them sit in a circle in a dark kitchen.

TELL them you have parts of a human body hidden in your kitchen.

HAND a grape to the friend sitting to your right and whisper to him "Here's an eye." Have him pass it on to his right saying the same thing.

CONTINUE doing this with other objects. Make sure to give them time to pass the objects to the next person around the circle. Use these or think of others yourself: cooked spaghetti for veins, slice of boiled egg for cheek, egg shells for nails, corn silks for hair.

Can they guess from touch alone what you used?

Seeing

Do both of your eyes see the same thing?

HOLD one finger in front of you.

LINE up your finger with some thing far away. Keep it steady.

CLOSE your right eye. Did your finger seem to move?

CLOSE your left eye. Did your finger seem to move?

It didn't seem to move much for one eye. That is your dominant eye. You have a dominant hand also. Are you right-handed? Are you right-eyed?

Eyes

Do your eyes change size?

PUT a hand mirror next to this book.

ROLL 10 sheets of white paper into a narrow tube. Put a rubber band around the tube.

SET the tube on a page of the book. Press one eye against the top of the tube. Close the other eye. Make sure you do not let light in from the top or bottom of the tube.

It will take a couple of minutes before you can see the print. Then look at both pupils in the mirror. The pupil of the eye you were using will be larger.

Part of your eye changes size. The pupil changes size.

Try this with a friend.

14

TAKE a hair from your head. Can you make it longer?

TAPE one end of your hair to a weight. You can use a quarter or an old key.

TAPE the other end to the inside of the lid from a glass jar. Screw the lid on the jar.

MARK the jar where the hair ends.

CHECK your mark for several days. Did the hair stretch?

Do the same experiment with another hair and another jar. Put a wet sponge or paper towel in this jar. Did this hair stretch faster or slower?

15

Heart

Can you watch your heart beat?

Your pulse tells you how fast your heart beats.

Can you find your pulse? Try your wrist.

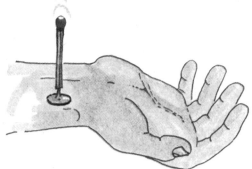

PUT a wooden kitchen match on a thumb tack.

PLACE the head of the thumb tack on the inside of your wrist.

WATCH the match bob for each beat. Want to see it bob faster?

JUMP up and down 75 times. Now watch it bob.

Temperature

Do you feel cooler on a windy day?

DIP some cotton in warm water.

DIP another wad in rubbing alcohol.

RUB one wrist with the cotton soaked in the water.

RUB the other wrist with the cotton soaked in alcohol. Which feels cooler?

Do it again. Blow on your wrists. Do they feel cooler?

How do you get cool on a hot day?

FeeLinGs & FacEs

LOOK at these faces. The lion looks mean. The dog looks sad. What do the other faces show? What made them look this way?

LOOK in a mirror.

MAKE faces to show how you feel at different times. At a party you may feel happy. You may feel angry when you have to go to bed early. If a big dog chases you, you may feel fear. When your mother hugs you, you feel warm and loving. Each of us has a lot of different feelings.

MAKE a mask to show opposite feelings.

DRAW a large circle on a paper bag.

CUT it out. Cut openings for eyes and a nose.

DRAW a face to show a feeling on one side.

SHOW the opposite feeling on the other side of the circle.

TIE string to the sides of the mask.

WEAR it to show how you feel.

MAKE animal masks to show some other feelings. How about—Sly as a fox? Mean as a bear? Happy as a lark?

TRY your own. Have a friend look at your masks and guess how you feel.

Map Your Head

What goes on in your head?

Are you thinking about food, a friend, a trip? A lot goes on in your head during a day. You can make a map of some of these things.

TAPE a large sheet of colored paper to a door or on a wall.

PLACE a strong light about 10 feet from the paper.

SIT in a chair so the light throws your shadow on the paper.

HAVE a friend trace your head shadow on the paper. Sit very still while he works.

TAKE down the paper.

FILL in your map. There are many ways to divide and organize your head map. Here are some ideas, but you can use all kinds of different things. What I like and what I don't like. What I want to be. What I do in a day. What my mother thinks I'm like.

TRY more than one.

CUT pictures from old magazines.

TEAR pieces of colored paper.

CUT words from old newspapers.

DRAW your own pictures.

USE these to fill in your map.

Personal Scrapbook

START a scrapbook about yourself.

USE a head map for the cover.

TELL where you live and what you look like.

PUT pictures of your family and pets in it.

TELL about all your favorite things.

NAME

ADDRESS

height
weight
Eyes
Hair

Me

MY PETS

DOG

CAT.

SPORTS

PICTURES OF MY FAMILY

DAD

MOM

BROTHER

SISTER

VACATION

SCHOOL

Crystals To See

PUT two charcoal briquettes in a shallow bowl.

MIX TOGETHER — 1/4 cup salt, 1/4 cup water, 1/4 cup laundry bluing, 1 tablespoon of ammonia.

POUR the liquid over the briquettes.

DO NOT COVER them entirely.

PLACE the bowl on a tray or plate.

SET it aside where no one will bother it.

WATCH! Check the dish in a day. See what happens as the dish sits.

TRY putting drops of food dye on the briquettes before you add the liquid.

Crystals To Eat

PUT 1-3/4 cups sugar in 1 cup boiling water, and let it dissolve.

LET cool to room temperature.

CUT two or more pieces of clean string.

TIE a paper clip to one end and tie the other end to a pencil or stick.

LAY the pencil across a glass or jar.

POUR the cooled mixture into the glass.

SET aside for a few days.

WATCH! What is beginning to form?

EAT the sugar crystals when ready. The longer the mixture stands the more candy crystals you will get.

25

Lemon Writing

WRITE a secret message to a friend.

MOISTEN a cotton swab on a slice of lemon.

PRINT a note to a friend on a white sheet of paper. Let it dry.

HIDE the note somewhere between the houses. How about hiding it under a rock or in a tree?

You can leave daily or weekly notes to each other.

TAKE the secret note from your secret hiding place.

SOAK it in water when no one is looking.

Pepper Magic

PUT some salt on your kitchen table or counter.

PUT some pepper on top and flatten it out with your finger.

Can you remove the pepper from the salt?

USE your pocket comb.

COMB through your hair several times.

HOLD one end of your comb about an inch above the pile and watch the pepper jump to the comb.

PUT one good shake of pepper in a fresh glass of water.

HOLD a slice of soap in the glass of water and watch the pepper move away.

Fire Extinguisher

GET these things together—1 small bottle, 1 straw, a cork, some thread, 3 tablespoons vinegar, facial tissue, and 1 teaspoon baking soda.

POUR the vinegar in the bottle.

PUT a hole through the cork.

PUT the straw through the hole.

UNFOLD the tissue and put the baking soda in the middle of the tissue.

FOLD up the edges of the tissue and tie it with thread.

HOLD the thread and put the tissue into the bottle. Do not let it touch the vinegar.

PUT the cork with the straw in it into the bottle. This will hold the thread.

TIP the bottle so the tissue gets wet from the vinegar. It will mix with the soda and form a gas.

POINT the straw towards a candle flame and watch what happens. The gas will put out the flame. Do you know the name of the gas?

The gas is called carbon dioxide. It is used in large fire extinguishers.

Bathtub Boats

TRACE your thumb on a piece of cardboard.

CUT out the small boat.

CUT a small slit in the back of the boat.

PUT a small piece of soap in the slit. This will make the boat move.

FILL your bathtub about an inch full.

FLOAT the boat in your bathtub. Don't make waves.

TAKE several wooden kitchen matches.

CUT OFF the heads of the matches and throw them away.

DIP one end of the matches in some cement glue.

MAKE sure the glue is hardened.

PUT fresh water in the bathtub. Carefully place the matches in the bathtub.

Your bathtub boats will move for several minutes.

Magic Glass

TAKE the glass from an 8 by 10 inch picture frame. Do this carefully.

STAND the glass on edge in front of you on a table. It must be straight up and down.

HOLD the glass up with stacks of books at each end. You can use pieces of modeling clay.

PUT the picture you want to copy between you and the glass.

PUT a blank white paper on the other side of the glass.

SHINE a bright light directly on the picture.

TURN OUT all the other lights in the room. The room should be dark. Only the picture should be lit.

SIT at the table facing the glass. You should see the picture reflected in the glass. The glass acts like a mirror. Move around a bit until you can see the picture on the glass.

REACH around the glass to draw on the blank paper. You can see your pencil and the reflected picture at the same time.

FOLLOW the reflection to draw a new picture on the blank paper. Sit still until you finish drawing.

PUT the glass back in the frame when you are done drawing.

Think of other pictures you can copy. You can make your own drawings. Copy trees from one picture, animals from another, and people from another.

Trashcan Archeology

FIND a full trashcan.

SPREAD newspaper all over the porch or somewhere your mother okays.

DUMP the trashcan on the paper.

SORT the trash and pretend you have just discovered it.

What can you tell about the people who live here? Can you find things that will tell you how these people live, and what things they enjoy doing?

When you do this, you are an R + KEY + ALL + OH + GIST. An archeologist is a person who finds out about the past by studying things people left behind.

CLEAN UP the mess.

36

FILL a trashcan with things.

ASK a friend to tell what kind of person lived here. What would a golf ball show? An empty tin can? A used tube of toothpaste? Think of others.

If you were digging, and found an old bow and arrow, what would that tell you about the person who left it?

If you found a cracked bowl with a picture of a cat on it, what would that tell you?

When people of the future find things we have left, what will that tell them?

37

Household Memory

How good is your memory?

CHOOSE a room.

SIT on the floor with a friend.

LOOK around you very carefully. Look at the furniture and the objects in the room. Do this for two minutes.

LEAVE the room while your friend hides something.

COME BACK. You have five minutes to name the missing object. Try this in other rooms. Let your friend try.

PLAY the game at your friend's home. See which one of you knows his home best.

Backyard Safari

HUNT animals in the wild. Join the fun. Any number can hunt.

CHOOSE someone to hide a stuffed animal in the back yard. The hunters shut their eyes. Don't peek.

HIDE the animal anywhere in the yard. Return to the group when it is hidden.

YELL "Bwana" and the hunt is on!

LOOK for the animal. When a hunter sees it, he sits down. The game ends when all are seated. The trick is to find the animal, but don't give it away to the other hunters.

The first one to see the animal gets to hide it next time.

Back Yard Pets

FIND earthworms at night in your yard or a vacant lot. The best time is after a light rain. Use a flashlight to spot them. Sometimes you can find them crawling on the sidewalk in the rain.

KEEP them in a large glass container. A terrarium would make a good home. You can use a fishbowl or a large, wide-mouth glass jar.

PUT gravel in the bottom.

ADD a few inches of top soil. It should be moist and loosely packed.

PUT your earthworms on top of the soil.

WATCH them. See what they do.

FEED earthworms coffee grounds and old lettuce. Cereals and cornmeal are good for them also.

MIX the food into the top layer of soil.

KEEP the soil moist, but not too wet.

STUDY your pets. Carefully dig them out of the soil.

PUT them on two layers of damp paper towels to look at them. Do they move away from you when you touch them?

TRY them on cold paper towels. Then put them on warm towels. Do they act the same?

TOUCH one with a piece of ice. What does it do?

COVER one with a damp paper towel for a few minutes. Then uncover it in a bright light. Does it try to hide from the light?

Leaf Stationery

COLLECT leaves from around your yard or park. Gather a variety of kinds and sizes.

USE a green ink pad. Place the leaf vein side down on the pad; cover it with another piece of paper and press.

REMOVE the paper and place the leaf on your stationery.

COVER with newspaper and press down.

REMOVE the paper and you have a leaf print. Decorate one corner or make a border around the paper.

LET nature make your stationery more personal and more beautiful.

Leaf Silhouette

PLACE the leaf directly on your paper.

WET a piece of cloth and rub across the ink pad.

HOLD the leaf firmly and dab around it with the cloth. This will make the outline of your leaf.

MOVE the leaf to a different position and repeat the process.

USE different colors of ink and create your own designs.

Wood Works

Key Chains

FIND a small piece of wood that has nice markings and looks interesting. Under a tree . . . on the grass . . . all around your yard are small pieces of wood. You can use some of these.

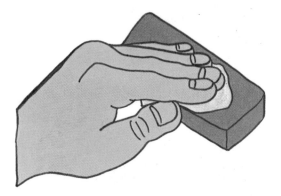

SAND it smooth with sandpaper. Make it smooth as glass. You may want to leave the bark around the edges.

DRILL a small hole in the top to put the chain through.

CARVE your name or someone else's on the wood. Practice on another piece before you carve the sanded wood.

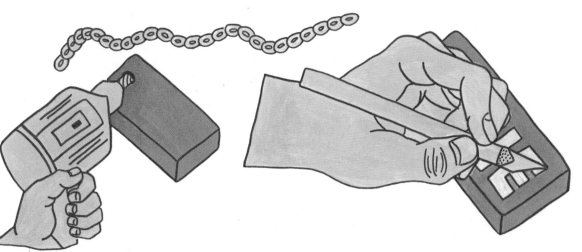

Name Plates

FIND a piece of wood and sand one side of it. Leave the bark on the rest of the wood.

WRITE your name with a pencil on the sanded side. This is your pattern.

BURN your name by writing with the sun.

POINT a magnifying glass at the smooth side of the wood. Direct the sun's rays at the wood until it begins to smoke.

MOVE the glass as you would a pen and it will write for you.

PRACTICE on another piece of wood before you write on the sanded one.

Use your name plate on your desk.

Weed Projects

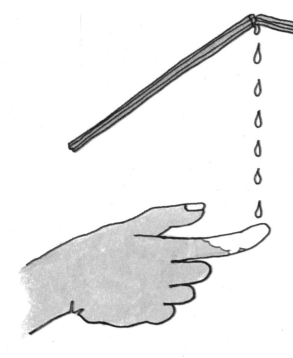

Do you have weeds in your yard? Try a nearby vacant lot or park for more weeds.

You can do a lot of things with milkweed and dandelions.

BREAK the stems open. Use the milky liquid to make a rubber band.

SQUEEZE about one teaspoon of liquid from the stem to coat your finger up to the first knuckle. Let it dry for several minutes. Then roll it off your finger.

MAKE a picture using a sheet of paper. Be sure to do this outside or on newspaper.

GLUE stems around the edge to make a frame.

MAKE a picture by using the lid of a box.

GLUE the weeds onto the lid.

SPRAY the weeds with hair spray.

Sheet Collection

TAKE an old sheet and put it under a big bush or small tree.

HOLD the corners and sides down with rocks.

SHAKE the bush or tree. See what falls on your sheet.

TRY leaving an old sheet under a big tree. See what drops on it in an hour, day or week.

KEEP a record of what you find on your sheet.

Do more things fall on your sheet in summer or in winter? In spring or in fall?

Do more things fall during the day or during the night?

Spider Art

SEARCH for a spider web in your yard or park. Early in the morning is the best time to find one. Look in low bushes or tall grass. Choose one that looks interesting.

SPRINKLE flour all over the web. Use just a little bit. You can shake the flour from a salt shaker. Be careful not to break the web.

HOLD a sheet of dark construction paper behind the web.

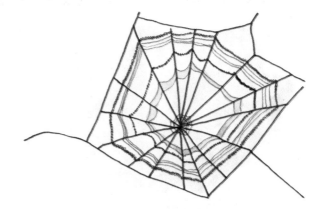

LIFT the web away with the construction paper. You have a spider web print on the paper.

SPRAY the print with clear plastic. Hair spray will work also. This will help protect your print.

HANG your spider art in your room. Or give it to someone as a gift.

OUTDOORS INDOOR

Nature projects that you have made yourself can bring the outdoors indoor. They can help you remember the insects of spring long after they have disappeared. They can remind you of the bright leaves of autumn when the trees are bare in winter.

COMMUNITY
YARD
HOME
ME

Your Own Phonebook

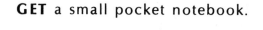

GET a small pocket notebook.

USE your telephone book to find the addresses and telephone numbers of these places in your community.
Fire Station
Police Station
Hospital
Doctor
School
Library
Church

WRITE the information you find carefully in your notebook.

PUT other important information in your phonebook.

Father's number at work
Mother's number at work
Your nearest neighbors' address and number.

You can also list your friends from school in your book. Put both their addresses and phone numbers.

Sometimes you need to reach someone in a hurry. Now you have your own phone book to use when you need it. You can carry it wherever you go.

Telephone Poster

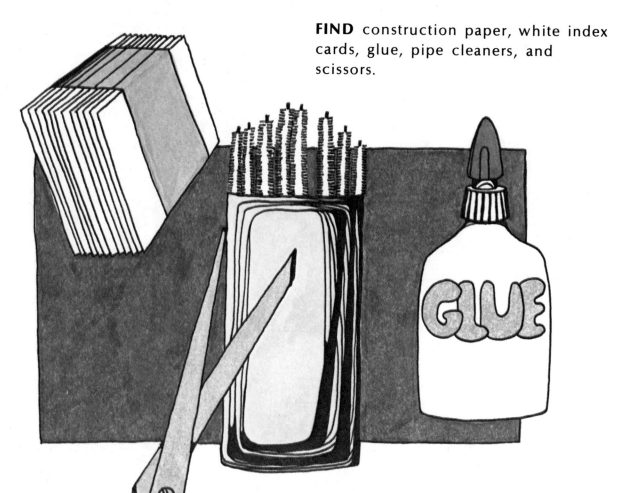

FIND construction paper, white index cards, glue, pipe cleaners, and scissors.

CHOOSE about six telephone numbers you might need in an emergency.

WRITE the name and number on a small strip of an index card.

ARRANGE these strips on a piece of construction paper.

GLUE the index cards to the paper.

DECORATE the poster by drawing a picture in the center of it.

MAKE a telephone from the pipe cleaners and put it at the top.

HANG your poster near your phone.

CHANGE the numbers by making a new card and gluing it over the old one.

BE SURE to keep your poster up to date.

Rubbings

GET some pieces of paper and a crayon.

PEEL the wrapping off the crayon.

TAKE one piece of paper. Hold it against a tree trunk.

RUB the side of the crayon over the paper.

LOOK at the interesting design the crayon makes. You have just made a rubbing.

MAKE a rubbing of a friend's ear. Try one of a sneaker bottom. Try one of a policeman's badge.

MAKE rubbings of bricks.

MAKE rubbings of other interesting things like old boards or the hood emblem of your car.

COMBINE lots of different things in one rubbing to make a picture for your room.

MAKE rubbings of the sides of houses around your neighborhood. Notice how they are different.

SEE how many different designs you can make from things in your neighborhood.

MAKE a book showing rubbings of all the things you have discovered. Maybe you'll find something secret.

61

Blindfold Tour

SIT in the middle of your yard with a blindfold on.

SEE how many sounds and smells you can identify.

GET a friend to bring you things like flowers, stones, sticks, or small pets.

SEE how many you can identify by feeling them.

BLINDFOLD a friend. See how many sounds and smells your friend can identify.

BRING your friend things to feel. See how many he can identify.

BLINDFOLD another friend. Count how many things she can identify by sound, smell, and touch.

BLINDFOLD several friends.

LEAD them carefully and safely around the block.

PICK OUT many different things for them to feel, smell, and listen to as they walk. See how many they can identify.

Sometimes your ears, nose and hands see things your eyes can't.

63

Dog Census

MAKE a bunch of cards that say THANK YOU FOR HELPING ME WITH MY DOG CENSUS. THANK YOU FOR TAKING SUCH GOOD CARE OF YOUR DOG. These will be Thank You cards.

MAKE another bunch of cards that say THANK YOU FOR HELPING ME WITH MY DOG CENSUS. PLEASE MAKE SURE YOUR DOG GETS REGULAR RABIES SHOTS. These will be your Reminder cards.

SIGN your name to all the cards.

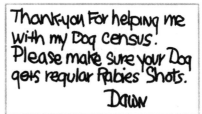

Thank you For helping me with my Dog census. Thank you For Taking such good care of your Dog. Jerry

Thank you For helping me with my Dog census. Please make sure your Dog gets regular Rabies Shots. Dawn

CALL an animal doctor on the telephone.

ASK him how often dogs in your neighborhood need rabies shots.

TALK to each of your neighbors. Tell them you are making a dog census. Be very nice.

ASK them if they have a dog.

ASK the dog's name.

ASK what kind of dog they have.

ASK if the dog has had its rabies shots.

WRITE DOWN the answers to your questions on a piece of paper.

GIVE them a Thank You card if their dog has had its shots.

GIVE them a Reminder card if their dog has not yet had its shots.

When you have finished your dog census, invite your neighbors to bring their dogs to a dog parade.

CANINE CENSUS FORM					
Address	No. of Dogs	Type	Name	Recent shot YES	NO
152 Hempstead	1	poodle	Truffles	✓	
211 Hill Str.	1	collie	Lad		✓

65

Sidewalk Sale

ROUND UP some of your friends.

PLAN a sidewalk or garage sale.

DECIDE where to have the sale. Pick a place where lots of people pass by.

CHECK with parents and get permission to use a garage or sidewalk. Have your sale on a weekday when most children might be home.

SEARCH through your old games, toys, and books. Repair any broken parts that you can. Replace missing parts to games. Bring all the sale goods to the garage the day before the sale.

LABEL each item with the name of the owner and the price. As you sell the goods you will know who gets the money.

ADVERTISE your sale. Make posters that tell where and when the sale is. Have a parade around your neighborhood to announce the sale. Show sample items on the poster.

SET up your tables and benches the night before the sale. Try to make your goods as attractive as possible. On the day of the sale you will be ready for the first customer.

KEEP all your money in a safe place.

TAKE turns making change. Remove all the tags from sold items. Later you can use them to divide your earnings.

If your sale is a success, why not plan a party to celebrate?

COMMUNITY MAP

TAKE a sheet of paper.

DRAW your block in the center. Use a square with an X in it for your house.

WRITE the names of streets around your block turning your paper as you write.

WALK around your block. Draw on your map squares for houses and rectangles for larger buildings like stores, apartments, or office buildings.

MAKE a map key. Put it in the lower left-hand corner.

USE different colors to show houses where you know the people.

TRY making up other symbols you may need.

You can keep adding to your map.

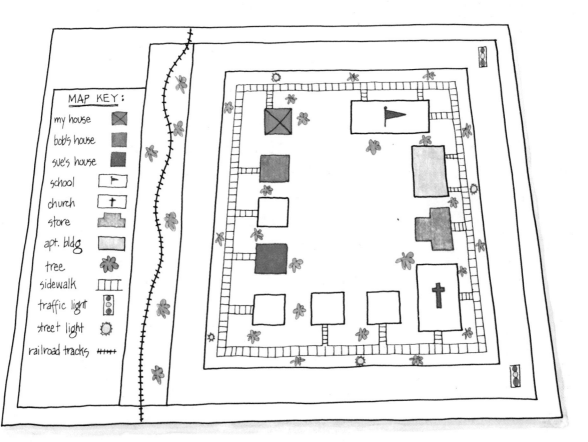

MAP KEY:

my house	⊠
bob's house	▨
sue's house	▨
school	⊢
church	†
store	▭
apt. bldg	▭
tree	✿
sidewalk	▥
traffic light	🚦
street light	☼
railroad tracks	+++++

Community Cards

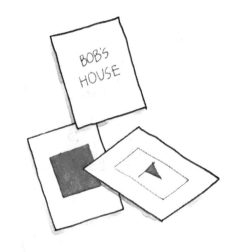

USE index cards to make your own card game. Use your map key to make matching cards.

If the yellow square were Bob's house, you draw a yellow square on one card. Write Bob's name on another card. For the school card use your principal or teacher's name. Make at least twenty matching cards.

MAKE one card that doesn't match. Use the name of someone in your neighborhood who you wouldn't want to be.

PUT your map key where everyone playing can see it.

DEAL out all the cards and play like "Old Maid."

Globe Clock

PLACE a globe or large ball such as a basketball or volleyball on a table.

STICK a dab of clay in the middle of the globe and put a pencil or toy soldier in it.

SHINE a lamp on the globe, then darken the room.

TURN the globe slowly and watch the pencil. It will move from a light area to a dark area. Which is day? night?

STAND in front of the globe and point to the right. That is East. Point to the left. That is West.

MARK East and West on the table.

PUT the pencil on the dark side of the globe and slowly turn it. In which direction does the sun rise? set?

PLACE the clay and pencil so the light shines directly on them. Is there a shadow? How large is it?

MOVE the globe slowly. What happens?

KEEP moving the globe until the pencil is in the dark. What happens to the shadow? When the shadow is shortest, it is noon. The shadow gets longer as the day gets shorter.

Sundial

TELL time by the sun.

CUT a piece of plywood 12″ x 12″.

MARK the hours of the day on the wood.

USE the picture as an example.

CUT a triangle from plywood. The further you live from the equator, the larger the angle must be.

GLUE the angle to the base so that it stands upright.

TAKE your sundial outside on a sunny day. Point the upright section to the north.

WATCH the shadow.

What does the shadow tell you?
What time is it? Why aren't there any
numbers on part of the base of the
sundial?

Why does the shadow move? Does it
tell you something about the earth's
movements?

USE your watch and the sundial
together. How close is your watch to
the sun?

People used a sundial long ago to tell
time. They knew that shadows moved
and they used this knowledge to tell
time.

Sun Alarm Clock

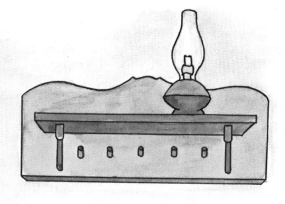

GATHER two blocks of wood, one flat for a base, the other for a pillar, six or seven marbles, a small metal tray, a birthday candle, a glass lens, some clay or wood and a coffee can.

USE one block of wood as a base. The other block and the candle can act as supports for the tray.

BALANCE the tray on the wood and the candle. Put the marbles on the tray. Line them up in a row.

CONSTRUCT the whole thing near a window where the morning sun comes in.

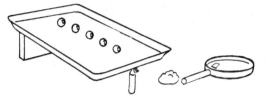

PLACE the coffee can under the tray.

MOUNT a magnifying glass near the candle. You can use clay to hold the lens, or you can use two blocks of wood to support it.

POINT the glass toward the candle. The sun will come through the glass, hit the candle and melt it. What will happen? Where will the marbles go?

Since the earth moves, it may be necessary for you to move your new alarm clock from time to time.

Water Clock

GET two empty coffee cans. Call one a Tanker. Call the other a Basin.

POKE a tiny hole in the bottom of the Tanker. A hammer and a small nail are good for punching small holes.

GET a piece of plywood. It should be a little wider and about as high as the Tanker.

MEASURE how wide the mouth of the Tanker is.

CUT two slots in the plywood exactly this far apart. The slots should be deep enough so the plywood will stand up solidly on the Tanker.

FIND a small block of wood that will fit nicely inside the Tanker.

ATTACH a long string to the block of wood with an eye screw.

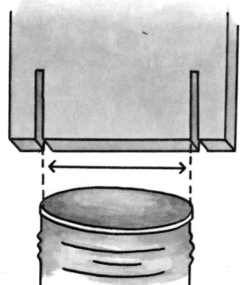

PUT two more eye screws in the top of the plywood. They should be just a little farther apart than the slots.

RUN the string through these eye screws.

TIE a weight to the end of the string. The weight must be lighter than the block of wood.

PUT two sticks across the mouth of your Basin.

PUT your finger over the hole you punched in the Tanker and fill the Tanker with water. The water should come up to the bottom of the plywood.

SET the Tanker on top of the Basin. The water from the Tanker will drip slowly into the Basin.

ATTACH a cardboard arrow with cellophane tape to the string near the bottom of the plywood. Make a mark where the arrow points. Each hour make another mark.

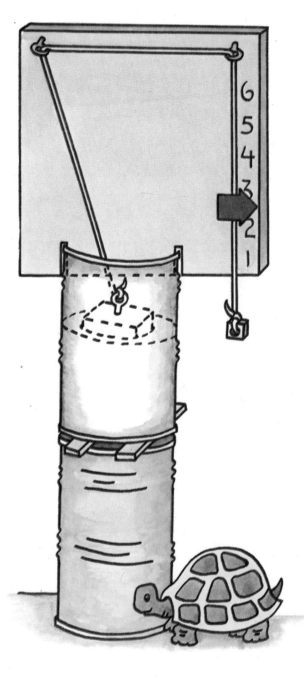

USE your water clock to time a turtle race.

Compass

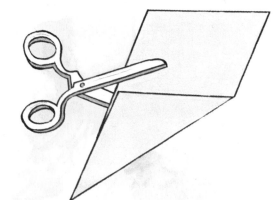

TRACE an empty lid on a sheet of paper.

MAKE a square piece of paper that is a little bigger than your lid.

FOLD it in half. Fold it in half again. Unfold your paper.

FOLD it this time to make a triangle. Make a triangle the other way using opposite corners.

PUT a mark on the edge of the circle at each fold mark.

LABEL the marks as shown.

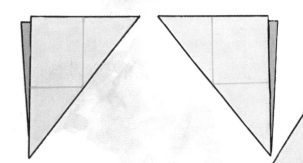

USE a magnet to make a compass.

HOLD the magnet in one hand and a sewing needle in the other.

STROKE the needle about 20 times in the same direction along one side of the magnet.

CUT a very thin slice of cork.

PUSH the needle through the cork and float the cork in your lid.

Your needle will point north.

PUT the lid on your compass rose with the needle pointing north.

Centrifugal Force

THREAD about a foot or less of cord or an old shoestring through a large empty spool.

TIE a light weight like a nut to one end and a heavier weight like two nuts to the other end.

HOLD the spool in your hand with the one weight end on the top. Get the top weight to spin by moving your hand in a small circle. The cord on top will get longer and the cord on the bottom shorter as you spin faster.

Spool Game

PUT a pencil or stick in the ground with a marshmallow lightly stuck on top.

SPIN the spool to try to knock off the marshmallow with the weight.

TRY it with smaller objects. Can you do it faster than a friend? Do you have the fastest spool in the neighborhood?

Balancing Tricks

CUT OFF the end of a raw potato.

STICK a sharpened pencil through the potato.

PUT two forks on opposite sides of the potato.

BALANCE the end of the pencil on the rim of an empty jar. Move the forks around a little until it balances.

EXPERIMENT with the top on a narrow jar.

TRY balancing the pencil point on the top.

TRY other balancing tricks.

Fossil Fun

COLLECT several objects around your home or yard.

POUR some plaster of paris into an old coffee can and stir in enough water to make a mixture that looks like heavy cream. Pour the liquid into an old aluminum pie or cake pan.

PLACE your objects in the plaster and press down. Remove them carefully. When the plaster dries, you will see an imprint of your objects.

MAKE a fossil picture for your room.

CHOOSE a shell, leaf, or other object.

MAKE a small cardboard frame and put it in the pie pan. Fill the mold with plaster and put the object in the center. Twist a piece of wire and put it at the top of the mold. Remove the object and let harden.

REMOVE the frame when the plaster has hardened. Paint the mold any color you wish and hang it by the wire.

SAVE animal tracks.

LOCATE a clear animal track in your yard or park.

PUT a cardboard frame around it and dust the print with a little powder or flour.

POUR some plaster of paris over the track and let harden.

REMOVE the frame and lift up the mold. What do you see?

START a collection for your room.

Salt Water to Fresh

USE ocean water if you can or make your own salt water.

TASTE the water to be sure it is salty.

POUR the salty water in a teakettle and boil it.

SEE the water vapor coming from the spout.

HOLD a small skillet above the spout.

CATCH the water from the bottom of the skillet in a pie pan.

TASTE the water you caught. Does it still taste salty?

Hard Water to Soft

TEST your water for hardness. Fill a pot with water. Put in one spoonful of soap. Try to make suds in the water for a couple of minutes.

FILL another pot with about the same amount of water. Get the water to boil on the stove for a few minutes.

WAIT for the second pot of water to cool. Put in one spoonful of soap. Now try to make suds in the water for a couple of minutes.

Which pot made more suds? Boiling softens water.

Water Watcher

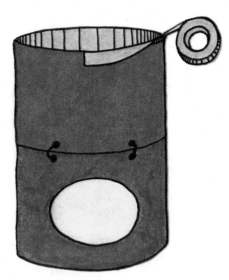

OPEN the ends of two tin cans. Use vegetable cans or coffee cans. Make sure they are the same size.

STACK the cans and wire them together.

MAKE small holes in several places and pull the wire through.

USE waterproof tape to cover the seam and one top part of one can.

PUT a glass or plastic bowl under the cans. It must be the same size as the cans. Put liquid solder around the place where the can and glass join.

TAPE the seam to make it waterproof.

TRY your water watcher in the bath tub to make sure no water can get in.

FIND a pond or stream near you.

LEAN over a dock or the bank and put the glass part of your watcher in the water. Look through the top can and you will be able to see life under the water. Why does your new invention make it easier to see under water?

USE your watcher anytime you are near water. It will aid you in finding fish when you are in a boat. You can study underwater life from the river bank or from a pier.

PADDLEBOAT

USE an old quart milk carton. Use the point of your scissors to poke a hole in each side of the carton. Stick a sharpened pencil through each hole.

WRAP a rubber band around the end of one of the pencils. Stretch it to the other pencil and wrap it around that end.

CUT a piece of cardboard from another milk carton to fit between the pencils. Stick the cardboard between the rubber band. Wind the cardboard toward the milk carton.

TRY your paddleboat in the bathtub.

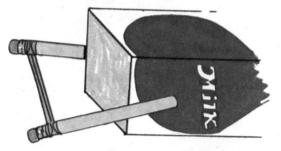

MAKE a fancy paddleboat with a paddlewheel. Slit two pieces of cardboard half-way. Fit the slits together.

CUT paper or index cards for the sides and top of the cabin. Poke four holes in the top of the carton the size of your cabin. Stick four toothpicks into the holes.

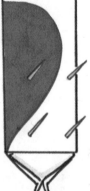

TAPE the cabin together. Glue your cabin to the toothpicks.

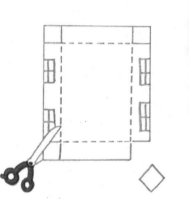

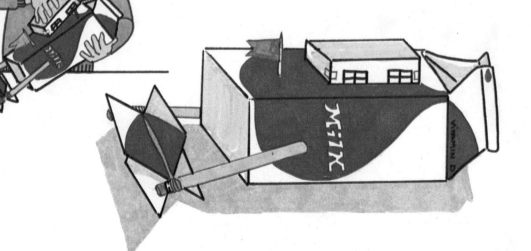

Hidden Things

FIND six hidden things in the water that need earth to live.

FIND seven hidden things on the earth that need water to live.

Tricks with Air

GET two empty drinking glasses and an aquarium with water in it.

PUT an empty glass in the aquarium and let it fill with water.

PUSH the second empty glass into the water upside down. Don't let any water get in.

RAISE the full glass upside down above the empty one.

TILT the empty glass so the bubbles go into the water filled glass.

You can pour air back and forth this way. That's because air takes up space.

GET a drinking glass and an index card.

FILL the glass with water.

PUT the card over the top of the glass.

HOLD the card in place with one hand.

TURN the glass upside down. Be sure you hold your hand against the card when you do this.

TAKE your hand away from the card.

The water will not fall out. That's because air presses against things very hard.

Wind Chimes

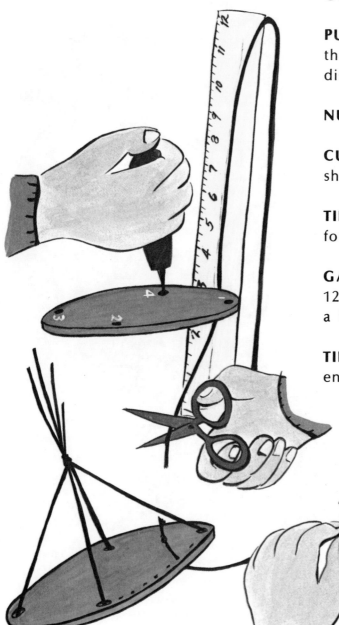

GET a plastic coffee can top.

PUNCH four holes in it, very close to the edge. The holes must be the same distance apart.

NUMBER the holes 1, 2, 3, and 4.

CUT four pieces of string. Each piece should be 24 inches long.

TIE one piece of string to each of the four holes.

GATHER up the four pieces of string 12 inches from the coffee can top. Tie a knot here.

TIE the four strings together at the end.

PUNCH seven holes an even distance apart around the edge between hole 1 and hole 2. Punch seven more between hole 2 and hole 3. Do the same thing between hole 3 and hole 4. Do the same thing between hole 4 and hole 1.

CUT twenty-eight pieces of light string about 10 inches long.

TIE one piece of string to each of the twenty-eight holes.

COLLECT twenty-eight old keys. Be sure they are keys no one needs anymore.

TIE one key to each piece of string.

HANG the chimes up in a breezy place.

You can also use old spoons, dog tags, or pieces of shell. You can use anything that tinkles when banged together.

Skate Sail

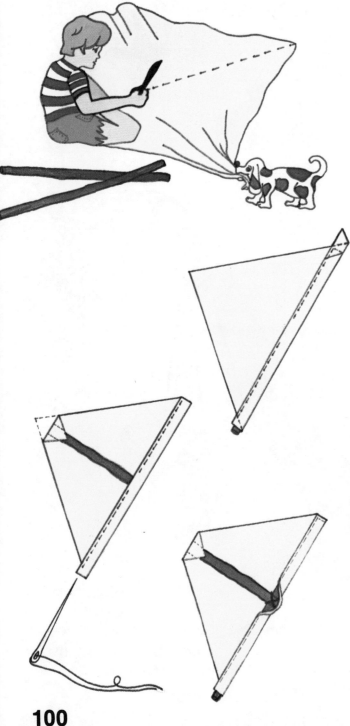

FIND an old double-bed sized sheet, two poles (one should be light like bamboo), and someone to help you with the sewing.

CUT the double sheet in two diagonally.

PLACE a light curtain pole on the long side of the sheet. Fold the sheet over the pole. Remove the pole and pin the sleeve to the sheet. Close the top of the sleeve and pin. Sew as shown.

ALLOW a 2″ to 4″ opening in the middle.

LAY the other pole across the sheet and measure a small pocket to cover it.

REMOVE the pole and sew.

PLACE the poles in the sail and tie them together where you have left the opening in the sleeve.

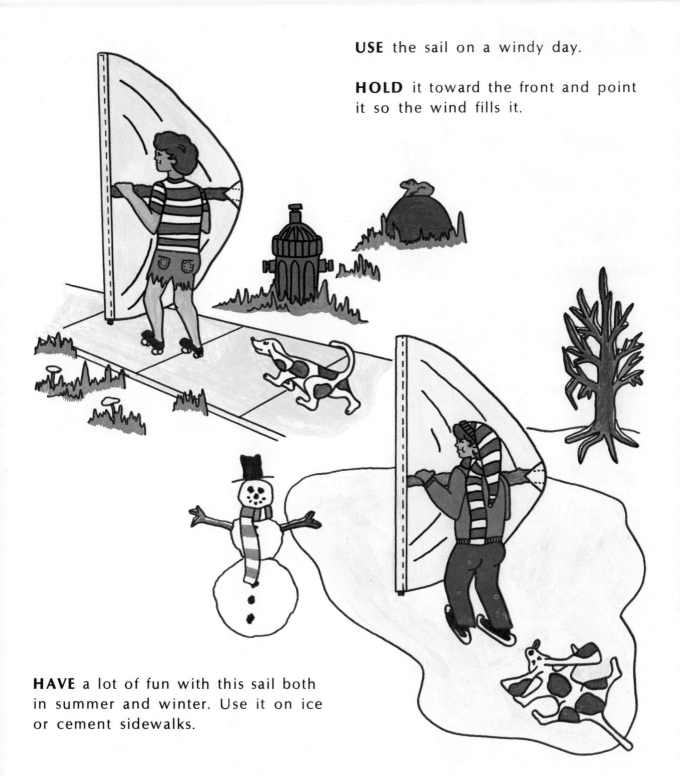

USE the sail on a windy day.

HOLD it toward the front and point it so the wind fills it.

HAVE a lot of fun with this sail both in summer and winter. Use it on ice or cement sidewalks.

MAKE a small one for a toy boat.

Clouds

LOOK at the sky.

FIND clouds that are very high and wispy. These are called cirrus clouds. They look like feathers.

FIND clouds that are very low and fluffy. These are called cumulus clouds. They look like pillows.

FIND some fluffy clouds that pile up on each other. They look like a tall pile of scoops of ice cream. When clouds like this turn black, they are called thunderheads.

Clouds form when warm air with moisture meets cooler air. That's why you can see your breath in winter. Each time you breathe out you make a cloud.

Making Clouds

FIND a gallon or a half gallon jug. Also get a stopper with a small hole in it.

RINSE the jug with warm water and put the stopper in.

BLOW as much air into the jug as you can. Blow through the small hole. Don't let any air out. Cover the hole with your finger.

PULL the stopper out quickly. A cloud will appear in the jug. Clouds on the ground are called fog.

RINSE the jug again and drop some lighted matches in. Put in the stopper and blow in air again.

PULL the stopper quickly.

Now you've made a thicker fog. Fog mixed with smoke is called smog. It is harmful if you breathe it a long time. Smog happens in cities with lots of factories. Watch out for smog.

Weather Vane

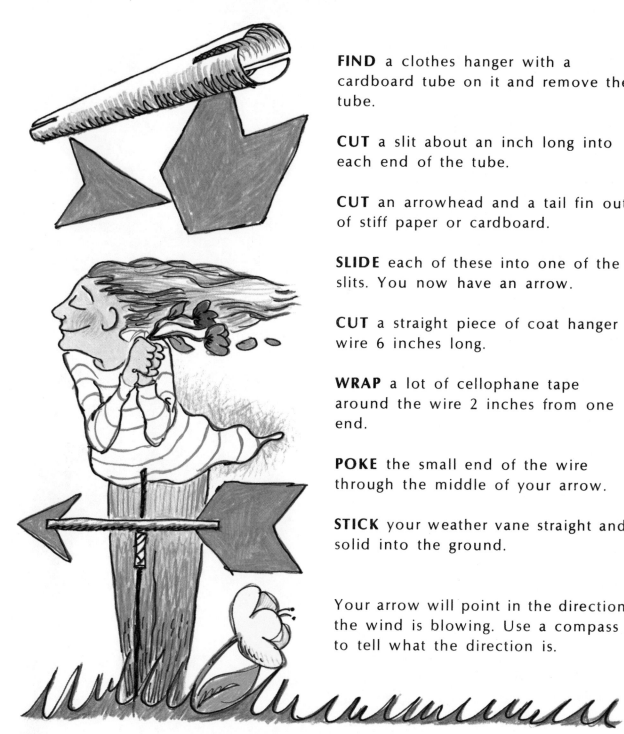

FIND a clothes hanger with a cardboard tube on it and remove the tube.

CUT a slit about an inch long into each end of the tube.

CUT an arrowhead and a tail fin out of stiff paper or cardboard.

SLIDE each of these into one of the slits. You now have an arrow.

CUT a straight piece of coat hanger wire 6 inches long.

WRAP a lot of cellophane tape around the wire 2 inches from one end.

POKE the small end of the wire through the middle of your arrow.

STICK your weather vane straight and solid into the ground.

Your arrow will point in the direction the wind is blowing. Use a compass to tell what the direction is.

Wind Anemometer

CUT two pieces of stiff cardboard 12 inches long and 1 inch wide.

CROSS the strips in the middle and glue them together.

STAPLE a paper cup to each of the four ends.

CUT a straight piece of coat hanger wire 8 inches long.

WRAP a lot of cellophane tape around the wire 2 inches from one end.

STICK the short end of the wire through the center of your cardboard cross.

STICK the wire straight and solid into the ground.

The cups will spin in the wind. The harder the wind, the faster the cups will spin.

Rain Gauge

FIND a wide mouth jar with straight sides and a tall, narrow bottle like an olive bottle.

POUR one inch of water into the jar.

POUR the water from the jar into the bottle.

MAKE a mark on the bottle where the water is. Use nail polish or put tape on the bottle you can write on.

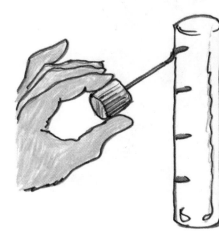

MARK the bottle into as many equal parts as you can. Each mark will be the same as another inch of water in the jar.

SET the jar outside when it rains to collect water.

POUR the rain water you collected into the bottle and notice how high it goes.

This will tell you about how many inches of rain fell.

Barometer

GET a glass jar with a wide mouth. Also get a balloon, two rubber bands, and a drinking straw. You'll also need cellophane tape, scissors and construction paper.

CUT a piece of balloon. Make it big enough to fit over the mouth of the jar.

STRETCH the piece of balloon smooth and tight over the jar mouth. Hold it in place with the rubber bands.

SNIP one end of the straw with scissors so it comes to a point.

TAPE the other end of the straw to the center of the balloon.

FOLD the construction paper into a triangular tube. Tape it together. This will let it stand up on one end.

PUT the tube next to the pointed end of the straw. Be sure it doesn't touch the straw.

MAKE a pencil line on the tube where the pointer points. Write the weather condition outside next to the line. Write stormy, rainy, cloudy, sunny, or whatever the weather is.

CHECK the position of the pointer once or twice a day. It will move up or down as the weather changes. Each time it moves, draw a line, and write down the weather.

After you've made some sunny and some stormy marks, you can predict weather. A barometer measures air pressure. When the pointer goes up, weather is usually cooler and clearer. When the pointer goes down, weather is usually warmer and the sky clouds over.

109

Weather Station

SET up your own weather station. Keep records and be your own weather man.

GATHER these instruments: rain gauge anemometer, thermometer and wind vane.

CHOOSE a sheltered place outside to be your station. A back porch or patio would make a good station.

ARRANGE your instruments so they will not be moved during your reporting.

USE a clip board to hold your records. Have a piece of paper for each of your instruments. Each day record your data. Do this at the same time. What do you have to report?

TRY this for a week and watch the changes. Try it for a month. Make a big calendar to show the weather each day.

111

GATHER all your weather information and put together your own forecast.

PRETEND you are a TV weatherperson.

WRITE a forecast that includes the amount of rainfall, the direction of the wind, the air pressure and the temperature.

REPORT the weather to your friends.

Wind Tunnel

REMOVE the tops and bottoms from nine milk cartons.

PLACE the cartons in three rows of three cartons. Tape them together.

PUT an electric fan behind your wind tunnel. Now you have an airstream.

MAKE an airfoil. Cut a strip of paper about 6 inches long and about half an inch wide. Bend it over and staple the ends together.

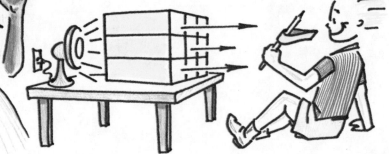

PUT a pencil through it and hold it in front of the wind tunnel.

TAPE ribbons on the tail and wings of a model airplane.

HOLD the plane in front of the wind tunnel.

TAPE ribbons on the sides of a toy block.

HOLD the block in front of the wind tunnel.

Sky Flyer

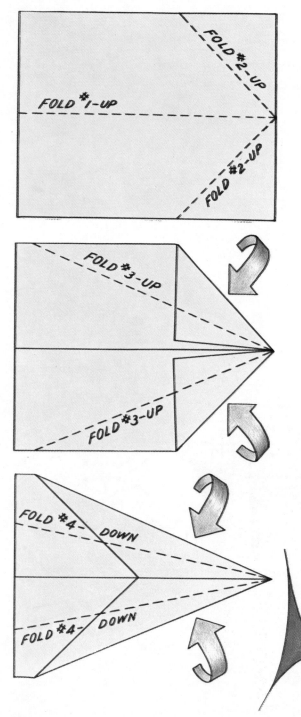

TAKE a regular size piece of paper.

FOLD it in half the long way. Call this Fold 1.

TAKE one corner and fold it down until it touches Fold 1. Call this Fold 2.

DO the same thing on the other side and make another Fold 2.

REPEAT this step again. Take the corner and fold it down until Fold 2 meets Fold 1. Do the same thing on the other side. This will make Fold 3 on both sides.

MAKE the wings by making a fold the full length of your plane. This will give you Fold 4 on both sides. The wider you make the back of your wing the more lift you will have. This lets the plane fly slower but longer.

MAKE trim tabs by tearing along Fold 4, starting at the back. Tear about 1/2 inch.

By folding your trim tabs up you will cause your plane to rise when you throw it. Folding the trim tabs down will cause the plane to nose over.

Folding one trim tab up will cause the plane to turn in that direction.

This kind of sky flyer is called a flying wing. It is great for racing.

Balloon Rocket

GET a balloon, a drinking straw, a spool of thread, and a needle.

CUT OFF about ten feet of thread.

THREAD a needle with the thread you cut off. Drop it through the straw.

TIE one end of the thread to one chair. Tie the other end to another chair.

MOVE the chairs apart carefully until the thread is tight. Be careful not to break the thread.

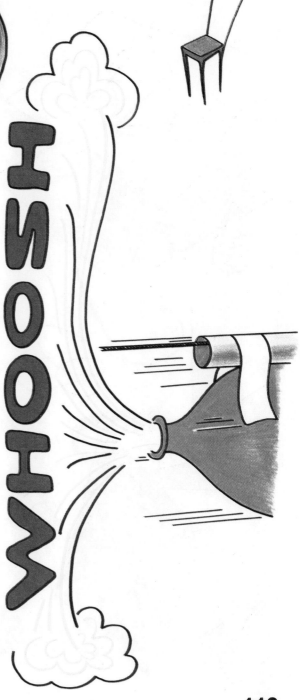

BLOW UP the balloon a couple of times to make sure you can blow it up easily.

TAPE the balloon to the straw.

BLOW UP the balloon and hold it closed.

MOVE the straw and balloon to one end of the thread and let go of the balloon.

The air escaping from the balloon will drive the straw very fast down the thread.

WHOOSH

Satellite Model

GET some light tracing paper, some dark construction paper, glue, a pin, and a long piece of string.

COPY the satellite pattern on the light tracing paper.

USE the copy you have just made to trace the pattern onto the construction paper. Save your tracing paper copy for making more models.

CUT OUT the pattern on the construction paper. Fold along the lines.

TRACE a solar cell pattern on construction paper. Make four panels. If you prefer, you can draw your own on the model.

GLUE the panels to the satellite. Be sure they are lined up evenly.

GLUE the tabs to the inside of the satellite.

PUSH a pipe cleaner through one heat panel and out the other. This is the satellite's antenna.

MAKE a small hole in the bottom of the satellite with a pin.

PUSH a knotted piece of string through the hole. Pull gently to make sure the string does not come out.

HANG the satellite from the ceiling of your room.

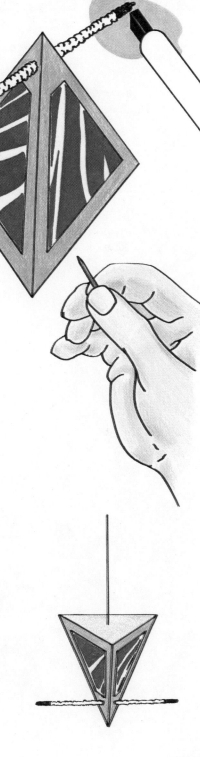

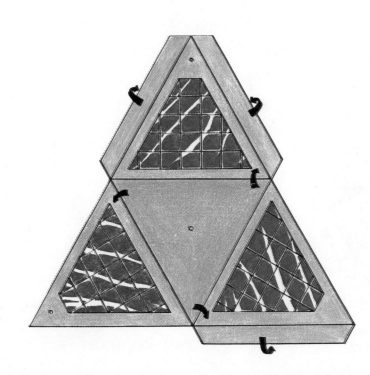

Telescope

FIND two cardboard tubes. They should be 24 inches long. One must fit snugly inside the other.

GO to a hobby store. Get two lenses. These should be the same size around as your tubes. Get one lens with a focal length of 24 inches. Get the other with a focal length of 2 inches.

GET some adhesive tape.

TAPE the 24 inch focal length lens to the end of the big tube. Tape the 2 inch focal length lens to the end of the small tube.

PUT the small tube inside the big one. Be sure the lenses are on the outside ends.

LOOK through the small end. Move the small tube in and out until the picture is clear.

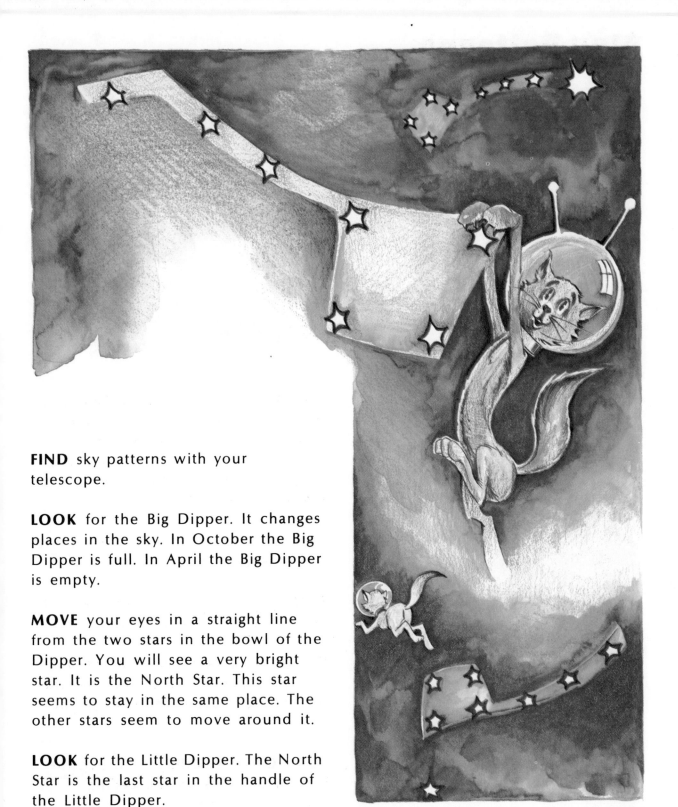

FIND sky patterns with your telescope.

LOOK for the Big Dipper. It changes places in the sky. In October the Big Dipper is full. In April the Big Dipper is empty.

MOVE your eyes in a straight line from the two stars in the bowl of the Dipper. You will see a very bright star. It is the North Star. This star seems to stay in the same place. The other stars seem to move around it.

LOOK for the Little Dipper. The North Star is the last star in the handle of the Little Dipper.

Star Patterns

STUDY these star patterns. Find one that looks like a big dipper. Find another that looks like a small dipper. Find others that look like a bear and a dragon. These are called constellations.

GET an old oatmeal box or cornmeal box. It should be tall and round.

PUNCH holes in the bottom that will make one of the star patterns.

GO into a dark room with the box and a flashlight. Point the box toward the ceiling and put the light in the box.

TURN ON the flashlight. Notice the pattern of lights on the ceiling.

124

PUT the round part of your flashlight on a piece of cardboard.

TRACE around it. Make as many circles as you want star patterns.

CUT OUT the circles.

PUNCH holes in each circle to make a star picture. Make a different star picture on each circle.

TAKE your cardboard circles and your flashlight into a dark room.

HOLD each circle tightly on the end of your flashlight and turn it on. Point it at the ceiling and notice the star patterns that are formed.

ASK a friend to identify each of the star patterns as you show them.

Umbrella Planetarium

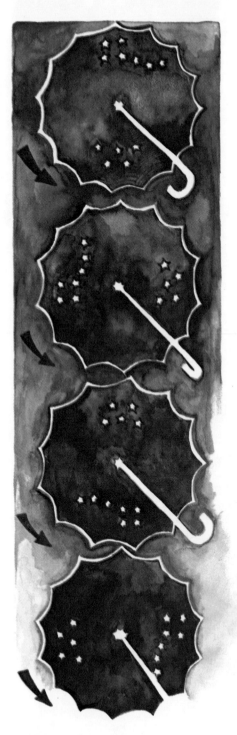

GET an umbrella, a pair of scissors, and some paper that glows in the dark. If you can't find this kind of paper, plain white paper will do.

CUT a lot of stars out of the paper.

LOOK at the star patterns to find out where to place your stars. Where the umbrella handle and the umbrella meet will be the North Star. All other stars seem to move around that point. When the Big Dipper is above the North Star, the W is below it.

TAPE or PASTE the stars of the Big Dipper and the W to the inside of the umbrella. The W is called Cassiopeia.

PUT the umbrella on the floor of a dark room or hold it over your head.

TURN the umbrella counter clockwise very slowly. This is how the stars appear to move in the sky during the year.

SHINE a flashlight on the stars if your stars do not glow in the dark.

ADD the Little Dipper to your planetarium. The North Star is in the handle of the Little Dipper.

ADD the Great Bear and the Dragon to your planetarium. The Big Dipper is part of the Bear. The Dragon is near the Little Dipper. The Dragon's tail is between the dippers.

ADD other star patterns to your planetarium by watching the sky and observing carefully. The best time to watch is usually just after the sun goes down.

Illustration Acknowledgments

ME
- 7: Thomas Petiet
- 8-13: Bettina Wood Tracey
- 14-15: Steven Roger Cole
- 16-17: Amy Hill
- 18-19: Joan Berg
- 20-22: Fred G. Baditoi

HOME
- 23: Thomas Petiet
- 24-25: Amy Hill
- 26-27: Bettina Wood Tracey
- 28-29: Sandra Laperriere
- 30-31: Daniel S. Cutler
- 32-33: Kaaren Klingel
- 34-35: Amy Hill
- 36-37: Jacqueline Sharp
- 38: Fred G. Baditoi

YARD
- 39: Thomas Petiet
- 40-41: Elizabeth MacGregor
- 42-43: Jacqueline Sharp
- 44-45: Cynthia M. Hammel
- 46-47: Fred G. Baditoi
- 48-49: Joan Berg
- 50-51: Bettina Wood Tracey
- 52-53: Cynthia M. Hammel
- 54: Amy Hill

COMMUNITY
- 55: Thomas Petiet
- 56-59: Joan Berg
- 60-65: Amy Hill
- 66-67: Jacqueline Sharp
- 68-70: Cynthia M. Hammel

EARTH
- 71: Thomas Petiet
- 72-81: Sandra Laperriere
- 82-83: Cynthia M. Hammel
- 84-85: Steven Roger Cole
- 86-87: Daniel S. Cutler
- 88-89: Bettina Wood Tracey
- 90-91: Joan Berg
- 92-93: Amy Hill
- 94: Elizabeth MacGregor

WEATHER
- 95: Thomas Petiet
- 96-97: Jacqueline Sharp
- 98-99: Kaaren Klingel
- 100-101: Fred G. Baditoi
- 102-103: Jacqueline Sharp
- 104-109: Steven Roger Cole
- 110-112: Jacqueline Sharp

Sky
- 113: Thomas Petiet
- 114-121: Alfred K. Becker
- 122-127: David LaVerne Laetz

DISCARD